Thrive in Marriage Participant + Leader's Guide

Internal design by Melissa Miller

Scripture quotations are taken from the HOLY BIBLE, NEW INTERNATIONAL VERSION. Copyright © 1972,1978,1984 by Biblica. Used by permission of Biblica.

Other Scripture quotations are taken from The Message. Copyright Â© 1993, 1994, 1995, 1996, 2000, 2001, 2002. Used by permission of NavPress Publishing Group.

Published by Married for A Purpose

8643 SE Seagrape Way

Hobe Sound, Florida 33455

Printed in, United States of America

ISBN:

Table of Contents

Thrive in Marriage
Leader's Guide for 6 Week Study

Dear Small Group Leader:

Thank you for facilitating and leading a group study of *Thrive in Marriage*. The following pages provide suggestions to lead this study.
A couple thoughts before you begin:

- Pray for each couple participating in your group. After all, God alone provides transformation. Invite Him to lead, direct and provide you with wisdom. He won't let you down.

- Second, access your weekly video for the class and preview it before your small group begins.

- Set a positive tone and structure for your group.

- Purchase Books and Participant Guides (to accompany this study) for your couples or encourage them to purchase the Correlating Book, *What I Wish My Mother Had Told Me About Marriage*, and the participant booklet at: https://marriedforapurpose.com/shop

Thank you for sharing your time, energy, and creativity. We'd love to hear the testimonies you encounter and any successes or practices that helped you enhance the facilitation of this study.

Week One

Preparation:
- Read Chapter 1
- If you have more than 10 couples, designate leaders to facilitate small group discussion. Allow a minimum of 3 couples per group and ideally no more than 5 per group.

ICE Breaker: Open each session with a time of fellowship and 'a get to know'

Interaction:
- Provide a 3-5-minute intro of your plan for the study and what you hope they will gain.

- Then, watch Surrender Completely: Video One. (The video lasts 14:59)

- Encourage each couple to answer the Questions Provided in their participant guide throughout the week. And, to use it as a tool for reflection and interaction as a couple.

- Before couples begin to share set the atmosphere by:
  - Encourage couples to only share what their spouse is comfortable with them sharing.
  - To keep their comments positive and forward moving.
  - And, depending on your group's size ... be mindful to set time parameters. You might use phrases like "IN 60 seconds or less, how would you answer this question?" Or if time permits you might say, "In 3 minutes or so, how would you answer this question?"

Week One's Suggested GROUP QUESTIONS:
1. Charles Swindoll once said "a good marriage isn't so much finding the right partner as it is being the right partner. And that starts with

you." How do you strive to be the right partner? Or in what ways do you want to grow to strengthen your marriage?

2. How do you intentionally put God first and surrender to Him in your everyday practices?

3. What is one action you want to implement this week from this first video lesson?

Before You dismiss, ASSIGN the following:
- If you didn't purchase Books and Participant Guides (to accompany this study) for your couples, encourage them to purchase the Correlating Book, What I Wish My Mother Had Told Me About Marriage, and the participant booklet for this study at: https://marriedforapurpose.com/shop

- Assign Chapters 2 and 3 for reading

- Point members to FREE ongoing inspiration provided at: www.Marriedforapurpose.com and www.facebook.com/marriedforapurpose

CLOSE in PRAYER

Week Two

Preparation:
- Read Chapters 2-3

ICE Breaker: Open each session with a time of fellowship and a 'get to know'

Interaction:
- Watch Video 2 Forgive Freely: (video lasts 12:50) then break to ask these questions:

Week Two's First Group of Suggested QUESTIONS: (If you meet for an hour, limit conversation to about 10 minutes of discussion for this section, before moving on to the next video.)

1. What do you think it looks like to forgive FREELY?

2. What helps you to extend forgiveness?

3. Stormie Omartian says: "the past should not be a place we live, but something from which we learn." What has been the greatest breakthrough for you as a couple or greatest lesson you've learned that has helped to strengthen your friendship with your spouse?

4. Greg and Julie shared the idea that what you feed grows and what you starve dies and that one of their best practices was to find what they LOVED about one another, not was LACKING in one another. What is your favorite quality or characteristic you love about your spouse?

5. What one way can we pray for you this week?

Next, Watch Video 3 Don't Shift the Blame: (video lasts 10:31) then break to ask these questions

Week Two's Next Group of Suggested QUESTIONS:

1. In Luke 6:36-37 The message bible reads: "Don't pick on people, jump on their failures, criticize their faults—unless, of course, you want the same treatment. Don't condemn those who are down; that hardness can boomerang. Be easy on people; you'll find life a lot easier. Give away your life; you'll find life given back, but not merely given back—given back with bonus and blessing. Giving, not getting, is the way. Generosity begets generosity." How have you experienced this verse in your life?

2. Andrew Murray wrote: (SLIDE) "Humility is not so much a virtue along with the others, but is the root of all, because it alone takes the right attitude before God and allows Him (as God) to do all." What is one practical way your spouse demonstrates humility?

3. Dale Carnegie said, "Any fool can criticize, complain, and condemn – and most fools do. But it takes character and self-control to be understanding and forgiving." How have you practiced self-control and stopped from shifting the blame to taking accountability for your own actions?

4. How do you practice intentional growth personally, or as a couple?

5. What one way do you want to grow this week based on this week's videos?

Assign:
- Encourage each couple to answer the Questions Provided in their booklets throughout the week. And, to use it as a tool for reflection and interaction as a couple.

- Assign Chapters 4 and 5 for reading

CLOSE in PRAYER

Week Three

Preparation:
- Read Chapters 4-5

ICE Breaker: Open each session with a time of fellowship and a 'get to know'

Interaction:
- Watch Video 4 Resist the Devil's Lies (video last 7:53)

Week three's first group of Suggested QUESTIONS: (If you meet for an hour, limit conversation to about 10 minutes of discussion for this section, before moving on to the next video.)

1. Greg and Julie Share: Some of the Enemy's most common lies in marriage are:

    a. *You deserve to be happy.*

    b. *It doesn't hurt to look.*

    c. *You deserve better.*

    d. *If your spouse really loved you, they would …*

    e. *Getting a divorce is no big deal.*

    f. *A true Christian marriage just happens … it doesn't take much effort. "*

    Have you ever struggled with one of those lies, and if so, how did God help you to overcome it?

2. CS LEWIS wrote, Love is not an affectionate feeling, but a steady wish for the loved person's ultimate good as far as it can be obtained." How has your spouse demonstrated unconditional love and helped you grow?

3. What are some practical ways the two of you grow together spiritually?

4. What helps you to overcome negative thoughts and resist the devil's lies?

5. What is one area we can pray about for you this week?

- Next Watch Video 5 Replace Unrealistic Expectations: (video lasts 8:55)

Week Three's Next Group of Suggested QUESTIONS:
1. Did anything stand out to you when Greg and Julie challenged us to think about the areas of our recurring conflict and to consider if they might stem from expectations of how our families did things as being the RIGHT way or because we determined that the way our family did things was the WRONG way of doing things?

2. How have you built on common ground to replace unrealistic expectations and you're your own godly expectations together as a couple?

3. Greg and Julie encourage us to Cultivate Connection by:
    o Stop focusing on your needs and start focusing on meeting your spouses'. How do you do that practically in your marriage?

4. They also encouraged us in the video to stay connected to God. How do you let God's love empowering you and your actions to revise your belief system and expectations, especially in areas that hold the potential of conflict?

5. In what area do you MOST want to focus on improving and how will do that practically?

Assign:
Chapter 6 and 7 for reading
Point members to FREE ongoing inspiration provided at:
www.Marriedforapurpose.com
www.facebook.com/marriedforapurpose

CLOSE in PRAYER

Week Four

Preparation:
- Read Chapters 6-7

ICE Breaker: Open each session with a time of fellowship and a 'get to know'

Interaction:
- Watch Video 6 Tame Your Tongue: (video lasts 9:55)

Week Four's First Group of Suggested QUESTIONS:

1. Greg and Julie share that to Enhance Communication we should: Practice praise instead of sarcasm. What are some of your best practices that help you to speak words of edification instead of sarcasm or disparaging comments?

2. They also encouraged us to be mindful of voice inflection. (I love you? Vs. I love you. VS. I LOVEEEEE YOU wink wink.) The inflection of our voice carries weight. How do you monitor your voice inflection as a couple?

3. I liked how they shared to NOT speak every thought or emotion in order to foster greater connection. What are some other best practices you've found that promote life, friendship, and connection in your relationship?

4. Greg and Julie also share ways they try to lift one another practically by offering loving words in the way one another received it. By speaking words that inspire one another to rise to the occasion. (like "you were made for this" or "you totally got this" or "no one can do …. Better than you.") And, finally, by

believing the best about one another. How do the two of you encourage and inspire the best in one another? OR

5. What helps to bring out your best?

- Next, Watch Video 7 Be Intentional: (video lasts 10:39)

Week Four's Next Group of Suggested QUESTIONS:

1. Greg and Julie share that Intentionality is defined as a trait of thoughtfulness ... in action or decision ... that Ensures we don't drift and get comfortable in our marriage. How do you INTENTIONALLY ensure that you don't get *comfortable* or *complacent* in your marriage?

2. They also share that in order to live intentionally in marriage, we need to put our spouse's needs above our own. What actions or in what ways have you watched your spouse put your needs above their own? How do you or your spouse live intentionally to put one another's needs above your own?

3. It's easy to say that we are Christians, but living it requires intentionality. How do you ensure your actions line up with your words?

4. Greg and Julie encouraged us to manage for what's most important. In this season of life, what is the most important thing you need to protect or 'manage for'? What are some things you 'manage for', in order to stay connected?

5. They also share that we must identify what to manage against the things that crowd out our time of connection; what one thing do you need to get rid of that is wasting your time or stealing your energy? What are some things that if you aren't careful will crowd your time of connection and how do you safeguard against that?

Assign:
Chapter 8 and 9

CLOSE in PRAYER

Week Five

Preparation:
- Read Chapters 8-9

ICE Breaker: Open each session with a time of fellowship and a 'get to know'

Interaction:
- Watch Video 8 Pursue Intimacy NOT just Sex: (video lasts 12:29)

Week Five's First Group of Suggested QUESTIONS:

1. Greg and Julie share that God Intended Sex To bring <u>oneness</u> in the marriage in body, mind, and soul. What are some NON-SEXUAL ways you communicate <u>desire</u> to your spouse?

2. How do you demonstrate a safe environment that promotes <u>vulnerability</u> and intimacy as a couple?

3. Describe your thoughts on God's desire for purity and intimacy in marriage? What does that look like to you?

4. How do you safeguard what GOD desires for sexual intimacy in your marriage?

5. What can we pray about for you this week?

- Watch Video 9 Fight FOR, NOT WITH Your Spouse: (Video lasts 8:36)

Week Five's Next Group of Suggested QUESTIONS:

1. Greg and Julie share God desires us to be <u>partners</u> in life, not <u>opponents</u>. To change from a <u>me first</u> attitude to a <u>we first</u> attitude. What are some best practices you have put into place that has helped you stay on the same team as partners and resist the urge to live as opponents?

2. What are some practical ways you live as "WE" instead of "ME" focused?

3. How does your spouse inspire your dreams?

4. What does your spouse do that makes you feel supported?

5. How can we pray for you this week?

Assign:
Chapter 10

CLOSE in PRAYER

Week Six

Preparation:
- Read Chapter 10

ICE Breaker: Open each session with a time of fellowship and a 'get to know'

Interaction:
- Then, Watch Video 10 Dare to Dream Together: (Video lasts 9:56)

Week Six's suggested QUESTIONS:

1. Greg and Julie remind us that, "God promises that when we ask anything in accordance with HIS will, we will have what we ask for. What one thing are you asking God for as a couple?

2. God desires us to believe for HIS best and to live into the dream HE designed for our life and marriage. He invites us to partner with HIM in that dream." What do the two of you dream about doing together as a couple?

3. If you aren't careful, what keeps you from pursuing your dreams together?

4. What are some best practices of ways you protect your dreams and live into them?

5. "What did you learn from this study and how do you plan to implement it?"

Assign:
NEXT GROUP OPPORTUNITY
Point members to FREE ongoing inspiration provided at:
www.Marriedforapurpose.com and
www.facebook.com/marriedforapurpose

Thrive in Marriage
Leader's Guide for 10 Week Study

Dear Small Group Leader:

Thank you for facilitating and leading a group study of *Thrive in Marriage*. The following pages provide suggestions to lead this study.
A couple thoughts before you begin:

- Pray for each couple participating in your group. After all, God alone provides transformation. Invite Him to lead, direct and provide you with wisdom. He won't let you down.

- Second, access your weekly video for the class and preview it before your small group begins.

- Set a positive tone and structure for your group.

- Purchase Books and Participant Guides (to accompany this study) for your couples or encourage them to purchase the Correlating Book, What I Wish My Mother Had Told Me About Marriage, and the participant booklet at: https://marriedforapurpose.com/shop

Thank you for sharing your time, energy, and creativity. We'd love to hear the testimonies you encounter and any successes or practices that helped you enhance the facilitation of this study.

Week One

WEEK ONE Preparation:
- Read Chapter 1
- If you have more than 10 couples, designate leaders to facilitate small group discussion. Allow a minimum of 3 couples per group and ideally no more than 5 per group.

ICE Breaker: Open each session with a time of fellowship and a 'get to know'

Interaction:
- Provide a quick 3-5-minute introduction of your plan for the study and what you hope they gain from it.

- Then, watch Surrender Completely: Video One. (The video lasts 14:59)

- Encourage each couple to answer the Questions Provided in their booklets throughout the week. And, to use it as a tool for reflection and interaction as a couple.

- Before couples begin to share set the atmosphere by:
  - Encouraging couples to only share what their spouse is comfortable with them sharing.
  - To keep their comments positive and forward moving.
  - And, depending on your group's size ... be mindful to set time parameters. You might use phrases like "IN 60 seconds or less, how would you answer this question?" Or if time permits you might say, "In 3 minutes or so, how would you answer this question?"

Week One's Suggested GROUP QUESTIONS:
1. Charles Swindoll once said "a good marriage isn't so much finding the right partner as it is being the right partner. And that starts with

you." How do you strive to be the right partner? Or in what ways do you want to grow to strengthen your marriage?

2. How do you intentionally put God first and surrender to Him in your everyday practices?
3. What is one action you want to implement this week from this first video lesson?

Before You dismiss, ASSIGN the following:

- If you didn't already purchase the correlating curriculum for your couples, encourage each couple to Purchase the Correlating Book, What I Wish My Mother Had Told Me About Marriage, and their participant booklets at: https://marriedforapurpose.com/shop

- Assign Chapters 2 for reading

- Point members to FREE ongoing inspiration provided at:
  www.Marriedforapurpose.com
  www.facebook.com/marriedforapurpose

CLOSE in PRAYER

Week Two

WEEK TWO Preparation:
- Read Chapters 2

ICE Breaker: Open each session with a time of fellowship and a 'get to know'

Interaction:
- Watch Video 2 Forgive Freely: (video lasts 12:50) then break to ask these questions:

1. What do you think it looks like to forgive FREELY?

2. What helps you to extend forgiveness?

3. Stormie Omartian says: "the past should not be a place we live, but something from which we learn." What has been the greatest breakthrough for you as a couple or greatest lesson you've learned that has helped to strengthen your friendship with your spouse?

4. Greg and Julie shared the idea that what you feed grows and what you starve dies and that one of their best practices was to find what they LOVED about one another, not was LACKING in one another. What is your favorite quality or characteristic you love about your spouse?

5. What one way can we pray for you this week?

Assign:
Chapter 3 for reading

Week Three

WEEK THREE Preparation:
- Read Chapters 3

ICE Breaker: Open each session with a time of fellowship and a 'get to know'

Interaction:
- Watch Video 3 Don't Shift the Blame: (Video lasts 10:31) Then break to ask these questions:

1. In Luke 6:36-37 The message bible reads: "Don't pick on people, jump on their failures, criticize their faults—unless, of course, you want the same treatment. Don't condemn those who are down; that hardness can boomerang. Be easy on people; you'll find life a lot easier. Give away your life; you'll find life given back, but not merely given back—given back with bonus and blessing. Giving, not getting, is the way. Generosity begets generosity." How have you experienced this verse in your life?

2. Andrew Murray wrote: (SLIDE) "Humility is not so much a virtue along with the others, but is the root of all, because it alone takes the right attitude before God and allows Him (as God) to do all." What is one practical way your spouse demonstrates humility?

3. Dale Carnegie said, "Any fool can criticize, complain, and condemn – and most fools do. But it takes character and self-control to be understanding and forgiving." How have you practiced self-control and stopped from shifting the blame to taking accountability for your own actions?

4. How do you practice intentional growth personally, or as a couple?

5. What one way do you want to grow this week based on this week's videos?

Assign:
Chapter 4 for reading

Week Four

WEEK Four Preparation:
- Read Chapters 4

ICE Breaker: Open each session with a time of fellowship and a get to know

Interaction:
- Watch Video 4 Resist the Devil's Lies (video last 7:53)
- Then, ask the following questions:
1. Greg and Julie Share: Some of the Enemy's most common lies in marriage are:

a.   *You deserve to be happy.*

b.   *It doesn't hurt to look.*

c.   *You deserve better.*

d.   *If your spouse really loved you, they would …*

e.   *Getting a divorce is no big deal.*

f.   *A true Christian marriage just happens … it doesn't take*

         much effort. "

Have you ever struggled with one of those lies, and if so, how did

God help you to overcome it?

2. CS LEWIS wrote, "Love is not an affectionate feeling, but a steady wish for the loved person's ultimate good as far as it can be obtained." How has your spouse demonstrated unconditional love and helped you grow?

3. What are some practical ways the two of you grow together spiritually?

4. What helps you to overcome negative thoughts and resist the devil's lies?

5. What is one area we can pray about for you this week?

Assign:
Chapter 5
Point members to FREE ongoing inspiration provided at:
www.Marriedforapurpose.com
www.facebook.com/marriedforapurpose

Week Five

WEEK Five Preparation:
- Read Chapters 5

ICE Breaker: Open each session with a time of fellowship and a 'get to know'

Interaction:
- Watch Video 5 Replace Unrealistic Expectations: (video lasts 8:55)
- Then, ask the following questions:

1. Did anything stand out to you when Greg and Julie challenged us to think about the areas of our recurring conflict and to consider if they might stem from expectations of how our families did things as being the RIGHT way or because we determined that the way our family did things was the WRONG way of doing things?
2. How have you built on common ground to replace unrealistic expectations and you're your own godly expectations together as a couple?
3. Greg and Julie encourage us to Cultivate Connection by:
   - Stop focusing on your needs and start focusing on meeting your spouses'. How do you do that practically in your marriage?
4. They also encouraged us in the video to stay connected to God. How do you let God's love empowering you and your actions to revise your belief system and expectations, especially in areas that hold the potential of conflict?
5. In what area do you MOST want to focus on improving and how will do that practically?

Assign:
Chapter 6

Week Six

WEEK 6 Preparation:
- Read Chapter 6

ICE Breaker: Open each session with a time of fellowship and 'a get to know'

Interaction:
- Watch Video 6 Tame Your Tongue: (video lasts 9:55)

- Then, Ask the following Suggested Questions

1. Greg and Julie share that to Enhance Communication we should: Practice praise instead of sarcasm. What are some of your best practices that help you to speak words of edification instead of sarcasm or disparaging comments?

2. They also encouraged us to be mindful of voice inflection. (I love you? Vs. I love you. VS. I LOVEEEEE YOU wink wink.) The inflection of our voice carries weight. How do you monitor your voice inflection as a couple?

3. I liked how they shared to NOT speak every thought or emotion in order to foster greater connection. What are some other best practices you've found that promote life, friendship, and connection in your relationship?

4. Greg and Julie also share ways they try to lift one another practically by offering loving words in the way one another received it. By speaking words that inspire one another to rise to the occasion. (like "you were made for this" or "you totally got

this" or "no one can do .... Better than you.") And, finally, by believing the best about one another. How do the two of you encourage and inspire the best in one another? OR

5. What helps to bring out your best?

Assign:
Chapter 7

Week Seven

WEEK 7 Preparation:
- Read Chapter 7

ICE Breaker: Open each session with a time of fellowship and a 'get to know'

Interaction:
- Watch Video 7 Be Intentional: (video lasts 10:39)
- Then, Ask the following Suggested Questions

1. Greg and Julie share that Intentionality is defined as a trait of thoughtfulness ... in action or decision ... that Ensures we don't drift and get comfortable in our marriage. How do you INTENTIONALLY ensure that you don't get *comfortable* or *complacent* in your marriage?

2. They also share that in order to live intentionally in marriage, we need to put our spouse's needs above our own. What actions or in what ways have you watched your spouse put your needs above their own? How do you or your spouse live intentionally to put one another's needs above your own?

3. It's easy to say that we are Christians, but living it requires intentionality. How do you ensure your actions line up with your words?

4. Greg and Julie encouraged us to manage for what's most important. In this season of life, what is the most important thing you need to protect or 'manage for'? What are some things you manage for, in order to stay connected?

5. They also share that we must identify what to manage against the things that crowd out our time of connection; what one thing do you need to get rid of that is wasting your time or stealing your energy? What are some things that if you aren't careful will crowd your time of connection and how do you safeguard against that?

Assign:
Chapter 8

Week Eight

WEEK 8 Preparation:
- Read Chapter 8

ICE Breaker: Open each session with a time of fellowship and a 'get to know'

Interaction:
- Watch Video 8 Pursue Intimacy NOT just Sex: (video lasts 12:29)
- Then ask these suggested questions

1. Greg and Julie share that God Intended Sex To bring <u>oneness</u> in the marriage in body, mind, and soul. What are some NON-SEXUAL ways you communicate <u>desire</u> to your spouse?

2. How do you demonstrate a safe environment that promotes <u>vulnerability</u> and intimacy as a couple?

3. Describe your thoughts on God's desire for purity and intimacy in marriage? What does that look like to you?

4. How do you safeguard what GOD desires for sexual intimacy in your marriage?

5. What can we pray about for you this week?

Assign:
Chapter 9

Week Nine

WEEK 9 Preparation:
- Read Chapter 9

ICE Breaker: Open each session with a time of fellowship and a 'get to know'

Interaction:
- Watch Video 9 Fight FOR, NOT WITH Your Spouse: (Video lasts 8:36)
- Then Ask the following Suggested Questions

1. Greg and Julie share God desires us to be <u>partners</u> in life, not <u>opponents</u>. To change from a <u>me first</u> attitude to a <u>we first</u> attitude. What are some best practices you have put into place that has helped you stay on the same team as partners and resist the urge to live as opponents?

2. What are some practical ways you live as "WE" instead of "ME" focused?

3. How does your spouse inspire your dreams?

4. What does your spouse do that makes you feel supported?

5. How can we pray for you this week?

Assign:
Chapter 10
Point members to FREE ongoing inspiration provided at:
www.Marriedforapurpose.com
www.facebook.com/marriedforapurpose

Week Ten

WEEK 10 Preparation:
- Read Chapter 10

ICE Breaker: Open each session with a time of fellowship and a 'get to know'

Interaction:
- Then, Watch Video 10 Dare to Dream Together: (Video lasts 9:56)

1. Greg and Julie remind us that, "God promises that when we ask anything in accordance with HIS will, we will have what we ask for. What one thing are you asking God for as a couple?

2. God desires us to believe for HIS best and to live into the dream HE designed for our life and marriage. He invites us to partner with HIM in that dream." What do the two of you dream about doing together as a couple?

3. If you aren't careful, what keeps you from pursuing your dreams together?

4. What are some best practices of ways you protect your dreams and live into them?

5. "What did you learn from this study and how do you plan to implement it?"

Assign:
NEXT SMALL GROUP STUDY
Point members to FREE ongoing inspiration provided at:
www.Marriedforapurpose.com
www.facebook.com/marriedforapurpose

"Come to me, all you who are weary and burdened, and I will give you rest. Take my yoke upon you and learn from me, for I am gentle and humble in heart."
Matthew 11:28-29

Session 1: Surrender Completely

The key to experiencing a thriving marriage is our complete surrender to God.

1. **Surrender is:**

    a. A lifestyle and constant <u>choice</u>.

    b. An intentional decision to put our <u>hope</u> and <u>faith</u> in God.

    c. An intentional decision to put our <u>confidence</u> in God alone.

> "If I put my trust in human beings first, I will end in despairing of everyone; I will become bitter, because I have insisted on man being what no man can ever be absolutely right. Never trust anything but the grace of God in yourself or in anyone else."
>
> OSWALD CHAMBERS

i

2. **Surrender in Marriage:**

    a. Exchanges our selfish nature for Christ's <u>servant-like</u> nature.

    b. Allows our <u>needs</u> to be fully met in Him so we can embrace marriage as He intended.

    c. Means surrendering our <u>rights</u> to God is non-negotiable.

"One does not surrender a life in an instant. That which is lifelong can only be surrendered in a lifetime."

ELIZABETH ELLIOT

ii

3. **Surrender Comes in Stages**

    a. It starts with our conscious decision to <u>submit</u>.

    b. Surrender is followed by our ongoing positive <u>actions</u>.

    c. The beautiful part of surrender is the great <u>freedom and healing</u> it delivers.

"A good marriage isn't so much finding the right partner as it is being the right partner. And that starts with you."

CHARLES R. SWINDOLL

iii

4. **Verses to Consider**

   a. 1 Peter 5:5 states, *"All of you, clothe yourselves with humility toward one another, because, 'God opposes the proud but gives grace to the humble.'"*

   In what ways does God wants you to serve instead of expecting to be served? What is one area you need God to heal in your marriage?

   _____

   _____

   _____

   _____

   _____

   _____

   _____

   _____

"If you want to have a happy marriage, be the kind of person who generates positive energy and sidesteps negative energy."

STEPHEN R. COVEY

iv

b. Hebrews 4:16 encourages us to *"approach the throne of grace with confidence, so that we may receive mercy and find grace to help us in our time of need."*

Is your first reaction to problems to complain to your spouse or call to God in prayer? Do you try to take control over the situation, or do you ask for God's wisdom and intervention?

_____

_____

_____

_____

_____

_____

_____

_____

c. *Philippians 2:3-5 states: "Do nothing out of selfish ambition or vain conceit, but in humility consider others better than yourselves. Each of you should look not only to your own interests, but also to the interests of others. Your attitude should be the same as that of Christ Jesus."*

What if we truly humbled ourselves and served as Christ served? What would your marriage look like if you chose to live at peace and preferred your spouse's needs over your own?

_____

_____

_____

_____

_____

_____

_____

Closing Prayer

Father, Intervene in my life and my marriage.

Empower me to surrender. Make this marriage better; I release it to You. Equip me to be the spouse You created me to be. I confess my sins, especially of trying to do things on my own. Lead me by Your Holy Spirit, and I will follow.

Make my marriage thrive, I pray, in Jesus' name, amen.

"Get rid of all bitterness, rage and anger, brawling and slander, along with every form of malice. Be kind and compassionate to one another, forgiving each other just as in Christ God forgave you." Ephesians 4:31-32

Session 2: Forgive, Freely

Forgive as God forgave you!

1. **The Power to Forgive:**

    a. Does not come through <u>self-will.</u>

    b. Does not come from through <u>suppressing</u> our feelings.

    c. Derives only from an <u>ongoing</u>, intimate relationship with Jesus Christ.

"God intended the marriage relationship to be a reflection of His relationship to us—a relationship that remains steadfast because it isn't based on fickle feelings or human worthiness but rather is based on uncompromising commitment."

SHANNON ETHRIDGE

v

2. **Our Relationship with God:**

   a. Changes our motives, thoughts, and feelings from the <u>inside</u> out.

   b. Empowers and compels us to love and extend <u>grace</u>.

   c. Reminds us who the real <u>Enemy</u> is.

"The past should not be a place where we live, but something from which we learn."
STORMIE OMARTIAN

vi

3. **When Couples Harbor Offenses:**

   a. It creates <u>physical</u> distance.

   b. It creates <u>emotional</u> distance.

   c. It creates <u>spiritual</u> distance.

"To be a Christian means to forgive the inexcusable because God has forgiven the inexcusable in you."

C.S. LEWIS

vii

4. Verses to Consider

    a. Jesus, while hanging on the cross, prayed, *"Father, forgive them, for they do not know what they are doing."*

Think to yourself; what's the worst thing you've ever done? Not to bring up your bad past, but simply to make note … God forgave you freely for that sin. His suffering on the cross provided your healing. How does Jesus' selflessness inspire you to forgive your spouse that freely?

_____

_____

_____

_____

_____

_____

_____

b. Matthew 18:18 states, *"I tell you the truth, whatever you bind on earth will be bound in heaven, and whatever you lose on earth will be loosed in heaven."*

If you hold on to offenses and fail to extend forgiveness, you bind that sin and offense to your heart and become paralyzed in its grip. In order for bitterness to be released, acknowledge that it exists. Don't oversimplify and just quickly say, "I forgive you." Forgiveness must be genuine.

Have you ever tried to will away your feelings or live in denial of them, only to find them resurfacing? Are there areas of anger, hatred, or discontentment you need to confess so God can heal you?

_____

_____

_____

_____

_____

_____

_____

_____

_____

_____

_

c. James 5:16 says, *"Therefore confess your sins to each other and pray for each other so that you may be healed. The prayer of a righteous man is powerful and effective."*

Are you bottled up, busy playing the perfect couple? Do you pretend you have it all together? Who is a godly couple you can go to for prayer and accountability?

_____

_____

_____

_____

_____

Closing Prayer

Father, I choose right now to release all the pain from my past. Help me to forgive and release my offenders.

I know harboring bitterness is not pleasing to You. Forgive me for trying to forgive in my own effort. Forgive me for trying to protect myself. I know You are my Defender. Protect me, Lord, in Jesus' name, amen.

"Do not judge, and you will not be judged. Do not condemn, and you will not be condemned. Forgive, and you will be forgiven. Give, and it will be given to you. A good measure, pressed down, shaken together and running over, will be poured into your lap. For with the measure you use, it will be measured to you." Luke 6:37-38

Session 3: Don't Shift the Blame

Don't shift the blame; take responsibility for your own actions.

1. **Taking Responsibility:**

    a. Shifts our focus from what our spouse did wrong to our own <u>actions.</u>

    b. Changes the way we <u>speak:</u> instead of "you" we start with "I."

"Any fool can criticize, complain, and condemn--and most fools do. But it takes character and self-control to be understanding and forgiving."

DALE CARNEGIE

viii

2. **Two Roads: Selfishness vs. Service**

   a. "Serve me!" vs. "I will serve <u>you.</u>"

   b. "I deserve…" vs "You deserve to be <u>loved and respected.</u>"

   c. "My needs are important." vs. "Your needs are <u>more important </u>than my own."

"Humility is not so much a virtue along with the others, but is the root of all, because it alone takes the right attitude before God and allows Him, as God, to do all."

ANDREW MURRAY

ix

3. **Questions for Growth:**

   a. "What could I have done that may have made a difference in the <u>outcome</u>?"

   b. "How can I <u>support</u> more and accuse less?"

   c. "Did I do everything possible to be a <u>good spouse</u> in this situation?"

"A wife is not responsible for her husband's life. She is responsible for her life. You cannot make your husband something he is not. Only God can do that."

CHARLES SWINDOLL

x

4. **Verses to Consider:**

a. James 4:1-2 says, *"What causes fights and quarrels among you? Don't they come from your desires that battle within you? You want something but don't get it. You kill and covet, but you cannot have what you want. You quarrel and fight. You do not have, because you do not ask God."*

Do you point out your spouse's faults? Do you try to manipulate him (or her) to think and feel the same as you?

_____

_____

_____

_____

_____

b. James 1:19-20 says, *"My dear brothers, take note of this: Everyone should be quick to listen, slow to speak and slow to become angry, for man's anger does not bring about the righteous life that God desires."*

Do you feel like you need to be God's mouthpiece? Do you speak more than you listen? Do you seek to understand or seek more to be understood?

_____

_____

_____

_____

_____

_____

_____

_____

"No love of the human heart is safe unless it has been satisfied by God first."

OSWALD CHAMBERS

xi

c. First Thessalonians 5:15-18 says, *"Be joyful always; pray continually; give thanks in all circumstances, for this is God's will for you in Christ Jesus."*

Do you pray more than you complain? Who do you turn to when you are frustrated? Will you entrust your spouse to God and ask Him to reveal what needs to be changed in you, meanwhile letting him address what your spouse needs to change?

_____

_____

_____

_____

_____

_____

Closing Prayer

Father, help me to take responsibility for my own actions and not shift the blame to my spouse. Help me to be all You ask, and help my spouse be all You desire. I give You every thought, feeling, and emotion. Create in me a pure heart. Cause me to walk righteously and with a loving, gentle spirit.

Make our marriage thrive, I pray, in Jesus' name. Amen.

"The devil … is a liar and the father of lies." John 8:44

Session 4: Resist the Devil's Lies

If you want to enjoy a marriage filled with friendship, laughter, and genuine love, you must resist the Devil's lies by embracing God's truth!

1. **The Devil:**

   a. Is like a <u>prowling lion</u>, the father of all lies, who steals, kills, and destroys. (Peter 5:8-9, John 8:44, John 10:10)

   b. Uses every opportunity to bombard our <u>minds</u> with lies (books, tv, worldly advice, etc.).

   c. Attempts to destroy the family unity through broken <u>marriages.</u>

> "Resist with the utmost abhorrence anything that causes you to doubt God's love and his loving-kindness toward you.
> Allow nothing to make you question the Father's love for his child."
>
> A. W. PINK

2. **Some of the Enemy's most common lies in marriage are:**

   a. *You deserve to be <u>happy.</u>*

   b. *It doesn't hurt to <u>look.</u>*

   c. *You deserve <u>better.</u>*

   d. *If your spouse really <u>loved</u> you, they would ...*

   e. *Getting a <u>divorce</u> is no big deal.*

   f. *A true Christian marriage <u>just happens</u> ... it doesn't take much effort.*

"I think a lot of the time we take relationships for granted. Because of that, we don't always give them the attention they deserve or require. But good relationships require a lot of effort."

JOHN MAXWELL

xiii

3. **The Truth About Marriage:**

   a. God wants you happy too but understands that <u>true happiness</u> begins by following <u>HIS commands</u> whether they're convenient to live or not.

   b. God knows; two are better than one and desires that we work in unity to live HIS purpose for our marriage.

c. Marriage is most enjoyed when we practice <u>unconditional</u> love and servanthood to our mate.

"Love is not affectionate feeling, but a steady wish for the loved person's ultimate good as far as it can be obtained."

C. S. LEWIS

xiv

4. Verses to Consider:

a. First Corinthians 13 describes love: *"Love is patient, love is kind. It does not envy, it does not boast, it is not proud. It is not rude, it is not self-seeking, it is not easily angered, it keeps no record of wrongs. Love does not delight in evil but rejoices with the truth. It always protects, always trusts, always hopes, always perseveres. Love never fails."*

Ask yourself: "Am I demonstrating love like this in my marriage? What changes do I need to make? How can I love more like Christ loves me?"

_____

_____

_____

_____

_____

_____

b. First John 4:16-21 records, *"God is love. Whoever lives in love lives in God, and God in him. In this way, love is made complete among us.... There is no fear in love. But perfect love drives out fear.... We love because he first loved us. If anyone says, 'I love God,' yet hates his brother, he is a liar. For anyone who does not love his brother, whom he has seen, cannot love God, whom he has not seen.... Whoever loves God must also love his brother."*

Now ask yourself: "Do I love like this, or do I impose conditions on my love?" List out the conditions you need to remove in order to love like God loves.

_____

_____

_____

_____

_____

_____

c. First Corinthians 10:6 warns us *not to set our hearts on evil things.* God always provides a means of escape from temptation. One of the best ways to avoid temptation is by instilling healthy boundaries. Women possess a keen sense for picking out potentially dangerous women, and indeed husbands need to pay attention. But, ladies, remember to heed your husband's warnings too. Your male friend from the office may entertain more than platonic thoughts, especially if he appears overly understanding and empathetic. Protective boundaries need to be put in place.

Do you need to pull away from any potentially dangerous relationships?

_____

_____

_____

_____

Closing Prayer

God, please forgive me for accepting any of the Enemy's lies. I know Satan aims to destroy my marriage; so God, please help me experience marriage as You intended. Heal and comfort my wounds.

Remove our stubbornness, our pride, our selfishness, and help us to forgive and love each other as You forgive and love us. Let us love one another in action. In Jesus' name.

"Trust in the LORD with all your heart and lean not on your own understanding; in all your ways acknowledge him, and he will make your paths straight." Proverbs 3:5-6

Session 5: Replace Unrealistic Expectations

Understand the origin of one another's expectations, and work to cultivate <u>realistic</u> expectations together.

1. **Expectations from our Upbringing:**

    a. We may decide we <u>want</u> to be just like them.

    b. We may vow we will <u>never</u> do things the way they did.

    c. Become a <u>part</u> of us, whether spoken or unspoken.

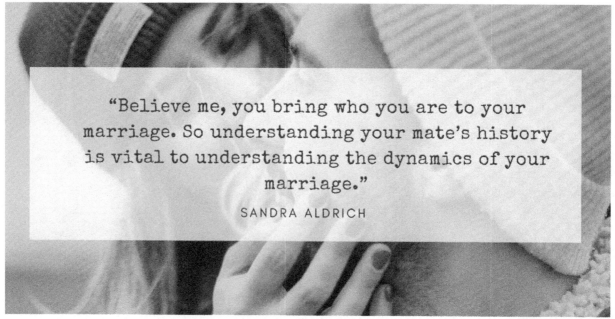

"Believe me, you bring who you are to your marriage. So understanding your mate's history is vital to understanding the dynamics of your marriage."

SANDRA ALDRICH

xv

Expectations often remain unmentioned because we aren't aware of what we've adopted as normal.

2. **In Confrontation:**

    a. Recognize where your conflicts <u>originate.</u>

    b. Decide together on <u>realistic </u>expectations.

    c. If an expectation is attainable and Biblical, then change; always try to meet your spouse's <u>needs.</u>

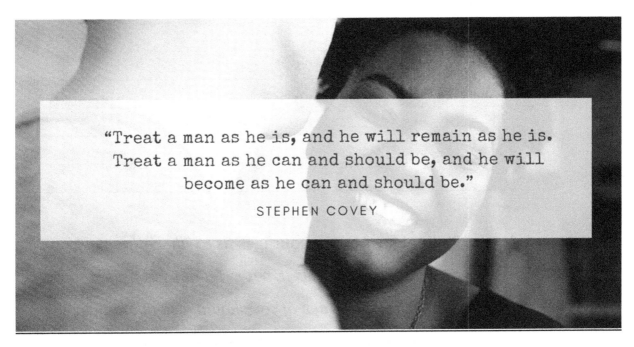

"Treat a man as he is, and he will remain as he is. Treat a man as he can and should be, and he will become as he can and should be."
STEPHEN COVEY

<u>xvi</u>

3. **Cultivate Servanthood by:**

    a. Stop focusing on your needs and start focusing on <u>meeting</u> your spouses'.

    b. Stay connected to God so His love is the one <u>empowering</u> you.

    c. Revise your <u>belief system</u> and expectations, especially in areas that cause conflict.

4. **Verses to Consider:**

    a. Colossians 3:17 says, *"Whatever you do, whether in word or deed, do it all in the name of the Lord Jesus."*

Do you serve your spouse based on their merit or God's? Remember, ultimately, God is the One we serve.

_____

_____

_____

_____

_____

_____

_____

    b. Philippians 2:3-4 encourages us to *"do nothing out of selfish ambition or vain conceit, but in humility consider others better than yourselves. Each of you should look not only to your own interests, but also to the interests of others."*

How can you demonstrate this kind of love to your spouse?

_____

_____

_____

_____

_____

c. Galatians 5:13-15 warns us to *"serve one another in love. The entire law is summed up in a single command: 'Love your neighbor as yourself.' If you keep on biting and devouring each other, watch out or you will be destroyed by each other."*

Are there any areas in which you haven't loved your spouse as yourself? Are there any ways you need to serve more like Christ?

_____

_____

_____

_____

_____

Questions to Ask

1. How would you describe your spouse's household? How does your spouse describe his father and mother? Were both parents present in the home? Did they practice gender-specific chores? How did your spouse's parents communicate with one another? How did they spend money? Who made the final decisions? Did the father or mother work all the time? The more we understand our expectations and their origins, the more likely we will resolve conflicts between us.

_____

_____

_____

_____

_____

2. What actions do you appreciate about your spouse? Or, what values do you wish they shared in common with you? Now, lest you break out in an argument—don't share your thoughts with your spouse quite yet, at least not until you process *the whys*.

_____

_____

_____

_____

_____

_____

3. *Why* do you wish your spouse managed finances differently? *Why* do you wish they showered you with gifts? *Why* is it so important that they believe or act in a certain way? *Why* is it their responsibility to wash the dishes (or some other chore)? *Why* are you frustrated at certain actions they do or don't do? Do any of your "whys" stem from your upbringing? Could there be an equally good (merely different) way of operating your household?

_____

_____

_____

_____

_____

_____

4. After evaluating your spouse's upbringing, take a moment to consider yours. Decide if your expectation is realistic by asking: Does this expectation line up with the principles taught in God's Word? If it contradicts the Word of God, then get rid of it. If the Word of God supports the expectation, then keep it. Look at it from a practical standpoint as well. Is it possible for you to meet your spouse's expectation? If it is ethical, balanced, and feasible, then why not compromise and choose to serve?

_____

_____

_____

_____

_____

_____

_____

Closing Prayer

Father, help me to walk in humility. Cause me to see the world not only through my own eyes, but also through Your eyes, and the eyes of my spouse. Help me humble myself and offer compassion toward my spouse.

May we surrender all of our expectations in exchange for Your sovereign will. Make our marriage thrive, I pray, in Jesus' name, amen.

"If anyone considers himself religious and yet does not keep a tight rein on his tongue, he deceives himself and his religion is worthless." James 1:26

Session 6: Tame Your Tongue

Control your tongue by allowing God to tame your <u>heart.</u>

1. **Our Words:**

   a. Come from the overflow of our <u>heart</u> (Matthew 12:34-35).

   b. Stem from thoughts of affliction or thoughts of <u>affection.</u>

   c. Are a reflection of where our <u>focus</u> is.

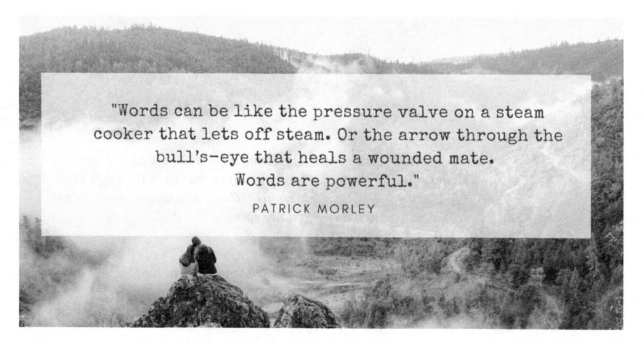

"Words can be like the pressure valve on a steam cooker that lets off steam. Or the arrow through the bull's-eye that heals a wounded mate. Words are powerful."

PATRICK MORLEY

xvii

2. To Enhance Communication:

 a. Practice <u>praise</u> instead of sarcasm.

 b. Be mindful of your voice <u>inflection.</u>

 c. Don't speak every thought or <u>emotion.</u>

"A few sincere words skillfully clumped together can lift the spirit of your partner high into the heavens."

PATRICK MORLEY

<u>xviii</u>

3. Bring out the best in your spouse:

 a. By offering loving words in the way they <u>receive </u>it.

 b. By speaking words that inspire them to <u>rise</u> to the occasion.

 c. By <u>believing</u> the best about them.

4. **Verses to Consider:**

    a. James 1:19 says, *"Everyone should be quick to listen, slow to speak and slow to become angry."*

One great checkpoint to help control your speech is asking, *Will this offense matter five minutes from now?* Try following it with a second question. *Will this matter five years from now?*

Ask yourself: "Do I tend to feel compelled to speak every thought? Do I speak every emotion? Do I feel the need to discuss every problem?" If so, ask God to help you not sweat the small stuff. On a scale from 1-10, write down where you would rate yourself on being quick to listen, slow to speak, and slow to become angry. What will you take from this lesson to help you improve that number?

_____

_____

_____

_____

_____

_____

_____

_____

    b. Proverbs 4:23-24 says, *"Guard your heart, for it is the wellspring of life. Put away perversity from your mouth; keep corrupt talk far from your lips."*

The most important aspect of controlling our speech is controlling our heart and thoughts. Ask: "What do I constantly focus on? Do my thoughts edify, lift up, and believe the best? Or do they tear down and believe the worst about my spouse?"

_____

_____

_____

_____

_____

_____

_____

"Death and life are in the power of the tongue, and those who love it will eat its fruit."

PROVERBS 18:21

c. In Matthew 22:37-40, Jesus says: *"Love the Lord your God with all your heart and with all your soul and with all your mind.' This is the first and greatest commandment. And the second is like it: 'Love your neighbor as yourself.'' All the Law and the Prophets hang on these two commandments."*

When we truly love God and allow Him to meet our needs, He refines our thinking and changes our character to be like His. We love more perfectly, and our speech reflects it. How can you show God's love to your spouse today through your words?

_____

_____

_____

_____

_____

_____

_____

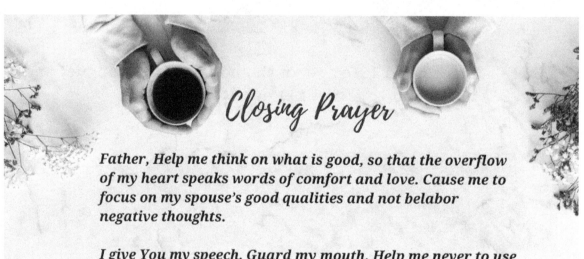

Closing Prayer

Father, Help me think on what is good, so that the overflow of my heart speaks words of comfort and love. Cause me to focus on my spouse's good qualities and not belabor negative thoughts.

I give You my speech. Guard my mouth. Help me never to use words that tear my spouse down. Make my marriage thrive I pray, in Jesus' name. Amen.

"If two lie down together, they will keep warm. But how can one keep warm alone? Though one may be overpowered, two can defend themselves. A cord of three strands is not quickly broken."
Ecclesiastes 4:11-12

Session 7: Be Intentional

Live <u>intentionally</u> to stay connected.

1. **Intentionality:**

   a. Is defined as a trait of <u>thoughtfulness</u> in action or decision.

   b. Ensures we don't drift and get <u>comfortable</u> in our marriage.

   c. Ensures our <u>actions</u> line up with our words.

New love is easy.
Happily-ever-after life is hard work."
DENNIS AND BARBARA RAINEY

xix

2. **To live intentionally in marriage:**

    a. We must put our spouse's <u>needs</u> above our own.

    b. We must identify what to '<u>manage for'.</u>

    c. We must identify what to <u>manage against.</u>

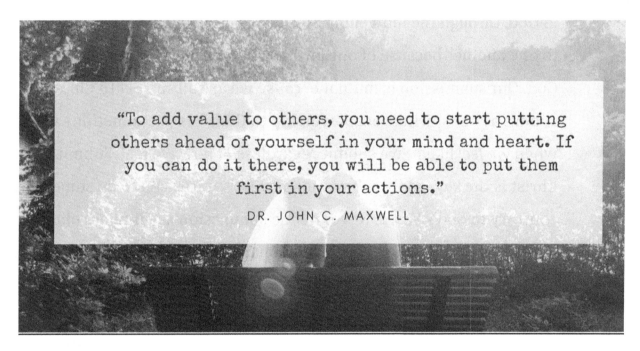

"To add value to others, you need to start putting others ahead of yourself in your mind and heart. If you can do it there, you will be able to put them first in your actions."

DR. JOHN C. MAXWELL

<u>xx</u>

3. **To Intentionally Connect:**

    a. Practice <u>scheduling</u> thoughtfulness.

    b. Practice being <u>fully present.</u>

    c. Practice <u>listening.</u>

4. Verses to Consider

    a. In Ephesians 5:21, Paul encourages married couples to *"submit to one another out of reverence for Christ."*

The Greek word *Phobos*, literally means fear or "reverential fear of God," "a wholesome dread of displeasing Him," "a fear that influences the disposition and attitude of one whose circumstances are guided by trust in God, through the indwelling Spirit of God." In simple terms, we submit to one another because of our love, devotion, and "reverential fear" of God. Our submission is mutual because we are all subject to Christ. We submit as our spiritual act of worship to God. It is not something we do when we *feel* like it; we submit regardless of how we feel. Submitting to Christ is the key; godly submission never requires you to do something contrary to God's Word. Never define submission as mindless obedience. How does this verse speak to you about intentionality in your marriage?

_____

_____

_____

_____

_____

_____

_____

    b. In Ephesians 5:22-24, Paul addresses wives by saying, *"Wives, submit to your husbands as to the Lord. For the husband is the head of the wife as Christ is the head of the church, his body, of which he is the Savior. Now as the church submits to Christ, so also wives should submit to their husbands in everything."*

God's Word instructs us to submit respect to our husbands because of the position that Christ gave them; our husbands hold the position as the head of our marriages (under Christ's rule.) In what way can you intentionally demonstrate respect?

_____

_____

_____

_____

_____

_____

_____

_____

"Marriage isn't about the final destination—the happily-ever-after with the person of our dreams. It's about the journey—getting there, walking together, enjoying the adventure en route to our final destination: a true sense of oneness with the other."

CINDI MCMENAMIN

xxi

c. Finally, in Ephesians 5:25-28, Paul instructs men: *"Husbands, love your wives, just as Christ loved the church and gave himself up for her to make her holy, cleansing her by the washing with water through the word, and to present her to himself as a radiant church, without stain or wrinkle or any other blemish, but holy and blameless. In this same way, husbands ought to love their wives as their own bodies. He who loves his wife loves himself."*

How can you apply this verse to living and loving intentionally in your marriage?

_____

_____

_____

_____

_____

_____

Closing Prayer

Father, make our love new. Give us the ability to serve one another in love. Help us enjoy one another again. Let us grow together instead of apart. Renew our commitment.

Alleviate any tension building between us. Let Your peace reign in my marriage, and cultivate a mature, life-giving atmosphere in this home. Cause my marriage to thrive, in Jesus' name, amen!

"The man and his wife were both naked, and they felt no shame." Genesis 2:25

Session 8: Pursue Intimacy, Not Just Sex

God wants you to say "Yes!" to your spouse, to love them, <u>body, mind and soul.</u>

1. **Sex is Not:**

   a. Dirty, a d<u>uty</u>, or something we should never talk about.

   b. A <u>free-for-all</u>.

   c. Meant to be separate from <u>emotional intimacy.</u>

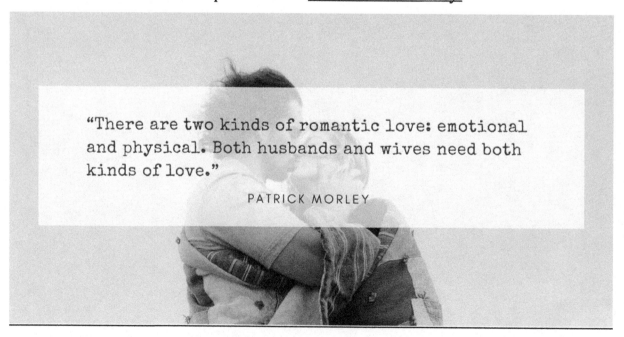

"There are two kinds of romantic love: emotional and physical. Both husbands and wives need both kinds of love."

PATRICK MORLEY

<u>xxii</u>

2. God Intended Sex:

a. To bring <u>oneness</u> in the marriage in body, mind, and soul.

b. To communicate <u>desire</u> to your spouse.

c. To share <u>vulnerability</u> and intimacy.

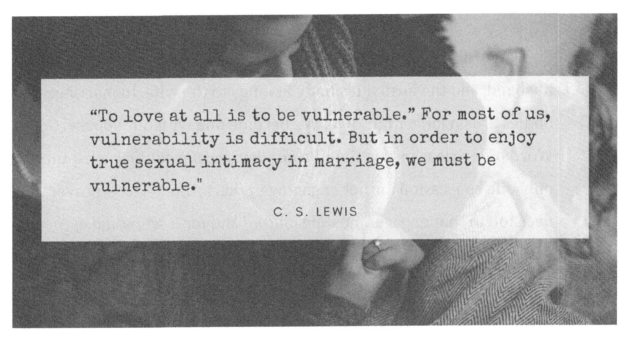

"To love at all is to be vulnerable." For most of us, vulnerability is difficult. But in order to enjoy true sexual intimacy in marriage, we must be vulnerable."

C. S. LEWIS

xxiii

3. Build Trust in Your Sex Life by:

a. Eliminating <u>pornography</u> or anything that could lead to unfaithfulness.

b. Harnessing <u>sexual energy</u> exclusively toward our spouse.

c. Relying on your relationship with God for purity, not <u>self-will.</u>

4. **Verses to Consider:**

   a. First Corinthians 7:3-5 states, *"The husband should fulfill his marital duty to his wife, and likewise the wife to her husband. The wife's body does not belong to her alone but also to her husband. In the same way, the husband's body does not belong to him alone but also to his wife. Do not deprive each other except by mutual consent and for a time…"*

God's Word goes so far as to say that the wife's body belongs to the husband, and the husband's body belongs to the wife. In marriage, our bodies are no longer our own. We become one with our spouse. God's Word offers clear instruction: *Do not deprive one another.* Scripture offers only one concession for not engaging in this intimate act—prayer. But the decision to "not engage" must be *mutual* and *for a set period of time for devotion to prayer.*

Ask yourself: "Have I used sex as a means of getting my way, by depriving my spouse as a means of punishment? Have I engaged all of my thoughts, emotions, and attention in my love-making to my spouse? Do I intentionally initiate and stay present—body, mind, and soul with my spouse in the bedroom?"

_____

_____

_____

_____

_____

b. Song of Solomon 1:4, the bride speaks to her beloved king and husband saying, *"Take me away with you — let us hurry! Let the king bring me into his chambers."* In Proverbs 5:15-19. Solomon encourages young men to *"drink water from your own cistern, running water from your own well. Should your springs overflow in the streets, your streams of water in the public squares? Let them be yours alone, never to be shared with strangers. May your fountain be blessed, and may you rejoice in the wife of your youth. A loving doe, a graceful deer — may her breasts satisfy you always, may you ever be captivated by her love."*

These Bible verses reveal God desire for us to woo our spouse as King Solomon did his bride. God's Word instructs us to uphold sexual intimacy within marriage—it is among the most precious acts any two human beings share together. Ask yourself: "Am I committed to being *present* in my love-making with my spouse? Do I celebrate their physique? Do I connect with them emotionally, completely? Do I try to satisfy their needs and make them feel wanted and loved?"

_____

_____

_____

_____

_____

_____

_____

_____

c. Hebrews 13:4 insists, *"Marriage should be honored by all, and the marriage bed kept pure."*

Ask yourself: "When making love, do I guard and reserve my thoughts for my spouse only? Do I allow my mind to drift to my to-do list? Do I focus on their face, or do distant and distorted thoughts fill my mind? Am I thrilled to be present with them? Do I give them my unadulterated respect and my utmost untainted integrity?" On a scale of 1 to 10, how would you rank your sexual intimacy with your spouse? Take a moment to consider how you can connect intentionally, sexually, as God intended the two of you to do.

_____

_____

_____

_____

_____

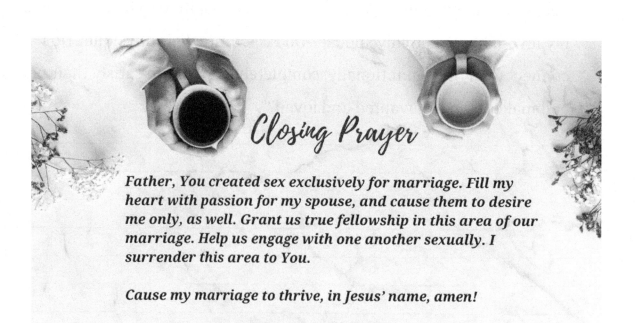

Closing Prayer

Father, You created sex exclusively for marriage. Fill my heart with passion for my spouse, and cause them to desire me only, as well. Grant us true fellowship in this area of our marriage. Help us engage with one another sexually. I surrender this area to You.

Cause my marriage to thrive, in Jesus' name, amen!

"Many a man claims to have unfailing love, but a faithful man who can find?" Proverbs 20:6

Session 9: Fight For, Not With, Your Spouse

The moment we stop growing is the moment we start dying.

1. **Fighting for Your Spouse Means:**

   a. Changing 'me first' attitudes to 'we first.'

   b. Making a commitment to never give up.

   c. Zero in on their needs and dreams.

"If you can't fly, run. If you can't run, walk. If you can't walk, crawl. But, by all means, keep moving."

MARTIN LUTHER KING JR.

xxiv

2. **Fight for Your Spouse Especially:**

    a. During life's <u>storms</u> and unexpected circumstances.

    b. When they've experienced <u>failure.</u>

    c. When they are discouraged, disengaged, and questioning their <u>value.</u>

"See that you humble yourselves, and take no place before God or man but that of a servant. That is your work; let that be your one purpose and prayer."
ANDREW MURRAY

xxv

3. **Practical Ways to Fight for Your Spouse:**

    a. Encourage them through life-giving <u>words.</u>

    b. Schedule a time to <u>laugh</u> and dream together.

    c. <u>Pray</u> and fast for your spouse.

4. **Verses to Consider:**

    a. Genesis 2:18 records, *"The LORD God said, 'It is not good for the man to be alone. I will make a helper suitable for him.'"*

Ask: "In what ways can I aid and accompany my spouse? What one way can I demonstrate that I am with them? Am I a suitable helper? Do I nurture positive growth? Do I express kindness and support?"

_____

_____

_____

_____

_____

_____

_____

"Each of us is born with an instinctive 'me first' attitude. But in marriage, each husband and wife has to cultivate a 'we first' mentality—and each needs to know that his or her partner shares that value."

TIM AND JOY DOWNS

xxvi

b. In 1 Corinthians 9:24-27, the apostle Paul writes, *"Do you not know that in a race all the runners run, but only one gets the prize? Run in such a way as to get the prize. Everyone who competes in the games goes into strict training. They do it to get a crown that will not last; but we do it to get a crown that will last forever. Therefore, I do not run like a man running aimlessly; I do not fight like a man beating the air. No, I beat my body and make it my slave so that after I have preached to others, I myself will not be disqualified for the prize."*

Ask yourself: "Have I become lazy? Do I run aimlessly, or am I intent to win this race, arm in arm with my spouse? Do I give our marriage and relationship all I have, or have I settled for merely going through the motions? Am I just pretending to run and putting up a good front, or am I pressing on to take control of my emotional responses and practicing fundamental steps to enhance my love for my spouse?"

_____

_____

_____

_____

_____

_____

_____

_____

c. In Philippians 3:12-14, Paul writes, *"Not that I have already obtained all this, or have already been made perfect, but I press on to take hold of that for which Christ Jesus took hold of me. Brothers, I do not consider myself yet to have taken hold of it. But one thing I do: Forgetting what is behind and straining toward what is ahead, I press on toward the goal to win the prize for which God has called me heavenward in Christ Jesus."*

In order to win, we must throw off every sin attempting to sever our relationship. Ask: "Am I fighting for my spouse, or am I still holding on to my pride, anger, or unforgiveness? How can I forget what lies behind and strain toward what God calls me to?"

_____

_____

_____

_____

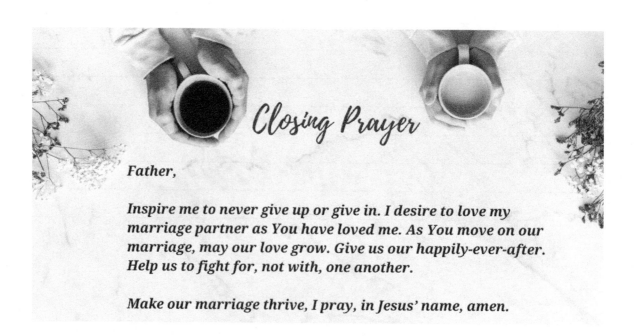

Closing Prayer

Father,

Inspire me to never give up or give in. I desire to love my marriage partner as You have loved me. As You move on our marriage, may our love grow. Give us our happily-ever-after. Help us to fight for, not with, one another.

Make our marriage thrive, I pray, in Jesus' name, amen.

"If two of you on earth agree about anything you ask for, it will be done for you by my Father in heaven." Matthew 18:19

Session 10: Dare to Dream, Together

You get what you <u>expect.</u> So, believe for the best!

1. **What keeps us from obtaining our dream together?**

   a. The enemy lures us to exchange God's best for <u>immediate</u> satisfaction.

   b. Fear of the <u>Unknown.</u>

   c. We forget to pursue <u>each other</u> while in pursuit of our dream.

"There are only two kinds of people in this world—the realists and the dreamers. The realists know where they're going. The dreamers have already been there."

ROBERT ORBEN

xxvii

2. How do we protect our dream?

    a. <u>Surround</u> yourself with the right people.

    b. Be a <u>safe place</u> and cheerleader for one another.

    c. Demonstrate <u>belief</u> in your spouse with your actions.

"Your time is limited, so don't waste it living someone else's life."

STEVE JOBS

xxviii

3. John Maxwell's questions to help define your dream:

    a. *"What would I do if I had no <u>limitations?</u>"*

    b. *"What would I do if I only had <u>five years</u> to live?"*

    c. *"What would I do if I had <u>unlimited</u> resources?"*

    d. *"What would I do if I knew I couldn't <u>fail?</u>"*

"Shoot for the moon. Even if you miss, you'll land among the stars."

LES BROWN

xxix

4. **Verses to Consider:**

   a. Proverbs 20:5 says, *"The purposes of a man's heart are deep waters, but a man of understanding draws them out."*

Ask yourself: "What keeps me from daring to dream with my spouse? What actions can I take to demonstrate my belief in my spouse? How can I inspire them to pursue their God-given purpose?

_____

_____

_____

_____

_____

_____

b. Second Corinthians 10:3-5 says, *"For though we live in the world, we do not wage war as the world does. The weapons we fight with are not the weapons of the world. On the contrary, they have divine power to demolish strongholds. We demolish arguments and every pretension that sets itself up against the knowledge of God, and we take captive every thought to make it obedient to Christ."*

Scripture commands us to focus our minds on Christ. So, ask yourself: "Do I demolish every pretension opposing God's truth? What attitudes do I communicate to my spouse? Am I influencing our relationship positively? How have my thoughts affected my spouse, our relationship, and our dreams?"

Do you encourage your spouse to shoot for the moon? Do you inspire their imagination? Ask them, "What do you think God wants for our lives? How can we move toward God's calling together? If given the opportunity, what do you want to accomplish in life?"

_____

_____

_____

_____

_____

_____

_____

_____

c. Ecclesiastes 4:12 states, *"Though one may be overpowered, two can defend themselves. A cord of three strands is not quickly broken."*

How have you compromised the strength of your relationship with your spouse or with God? Have you committed and contributed to the strength of your marriage? Have you given your spouse the support they need, or taken time to dream with them about their dreams?

_____

_____

_____

_____

Closing Prayer

Father,

Help us to dream together and support one another in those dreams. Help us to guard our thoughts to protect our God given dreams. Help us to continually inspire one another.

Make our marriage thrive, I pray, in Jesus' name, amen!

We'd love to hear how this study impacted you and your spouse. Share your testimony or contact us at: gregandjulie@marriedforapurpose.com
Find more couple's studies and resources at: https://marriedforapurpose.com/shop/
Connect with us Facebook at: www.Facebook.com/marriedforapurpose

END NOTES

[i] Oswald Chambers, *My Utmost for His Highest* (Westwood, N. J.: Barbour, 1935), 31 May.

[ii] www.goodreads.com/quotes/tag/surrender

[iii] Charles R. Swindoll, *Hope Again* (Dallas: Word, 1996), 110.

[iv] Stephen R. Covey, *The 7 Habits of Highly Effective People*. (New York: Free Press, 2004), 43.

[v] Shannon Ethridge, *Every Woman's Marriage* (Colorado Springs: Waterbrook, 2006), 38.

[vi] Omartian, *The Power of a Praying Wife*, 144.

[vii] www.goodreads.com/quotes/tag/forgiveness

[viii] www.goodreads.com/work/quotes/2370171-how-to-win-friends-and-influence-people

[ix] Andrew Murray. *Humility: The Journey toward Holiness* (Minneapolis: Bethany, 2001), 17.

[x] Swindoll, *Hope Again,* 103.

[xi] proverbsway.com/2013/07/08/hands-down-the-top-15-quotes-by-oswald-chambers

[xii] http://christian-quotes.ochristian.com/christian-quotes_ochristian.cgi?query=lies&action=Search&x=0&y=0

[xiii] http://johnmaxwellonleadership.com/2013/02/19/managing-the-disciplines-of-relationship-building/

[xiv] www.goodreads.com/author/quotes/1069006.C_S_Lewis

[xv] Aldrich, *Men Read Newspapers, Not Minds,* 72.

[xvi] www.goodreads.com/quotes/tag/expectations?page=2

[xvii] Patrick Morley, *Devotions for Couples* (Grand Rapids, Mich.: Zondervan, 1994), 60.

[xviii] Patrick Morley, *Devotions for Couples,* (Grand Rapids, Mich.: Zondervan, 1994), 60.

[xix] Dennis and Barbara Rainey, *Rekindling the Romance: Loving the Love of Your* Life (Nashville: Thomas Nelson, 2004), 35.

[xx] http://johnmaxwellonleadership.com/2009/08/21/todays-daily-reader-put-others-first/

[xxi] Cindi and Hugh McMenamin, *When Couples Walk Together: 31 Days to a Closer Connection* (Eugene, Ore.: Harvest, 2012), 11.

[xxii] Patrick Morley, *Devotions for Couples,* (Grand Rapids, Mich.: Zondervan, 1994), 102.

[xxiii] http://www.goodreads.com/work/quotes/14816053-the-four-loves

[xxiv] www.goodreads.com/quotes/495851-if-you-can-t-fly-run-if-you-can-t-run-walk

[xxv] Murray, *Humility: The Journey toward Holiness.* 17.

[xxvi] Downs, *The Seven Conflicts,* Chicago: Moody, 2003, 62.

[xxvii] Dr. John C. Maxwell, *Put Your Dream to the Test* (Nashville: Thomas Nelson, 2009), xxii.

[xxviii] www.quotationspage.com/quote/38353.html

[xxix] www.goodreads.com/quotes/4324-shoot-for-the-moon-even-if-you-miss-you-ll-land

Made in the USA
Monee, IL
09 October 2023

44260421R00057